This book belongs to

....

Copyright © 2015
make believe ideas ltd
The Wilderness, Berkhamsted, Hertfordshire, HP4 2AZ, UK.

www.makebelieveideas.com

Illustrated by Dawn Machell.
Designed by Jane Horne.

ONE
OF A KIND

Dawn Machell & Jane Horne

make
believe
ideas

PUPS ON PARADE

The proud little PUPPIES are out on PARADE.

With big, wagging TAILS,

they're a BARKING brigade!

LOOK up and down and try to find

which orange animal is ONE OF A KIND?

Who's got a BALL?   Who's wearing a stripy COAT?   Who's chewing a BONE?

Who's won a PRIZE? Who's ASLEEP? Who's chewing a SLIPPER?

HEY, HO, LET'S GO!

It's **BUSY** and *NOISY* on the big street.
The **SIRENS** go **NEE-NAH**
and the *CARS* go **BEEP-BEEP!**
LOOK up and down and try to find
which yellow vehicle is **ONE OF A KIND?**

Which MOTORBIKE has a PASSENGER?   Who's facing the WRONG way?

Who has a flashing LIGHT? ~ Who's lost a WHEEL? ~ Who's delivering ICE CREAM?

TEDDY BEARS'
PICNIC

Out in the sunlight, the **TEDDY BEARS** play.
They've packed up some **TREATS**
for their **PICNIC** today!
LOOK up and down and try to find
which woodland creature is **ONE OF A KIND?**

Who's eating a **CAKE?**   Who has a **PICNIC BASKET?**   Who's **GROWLING?**

Who's eating an APPLE? ∿ Who's holding a FLOWER? ∿ Who's eating some PIE?

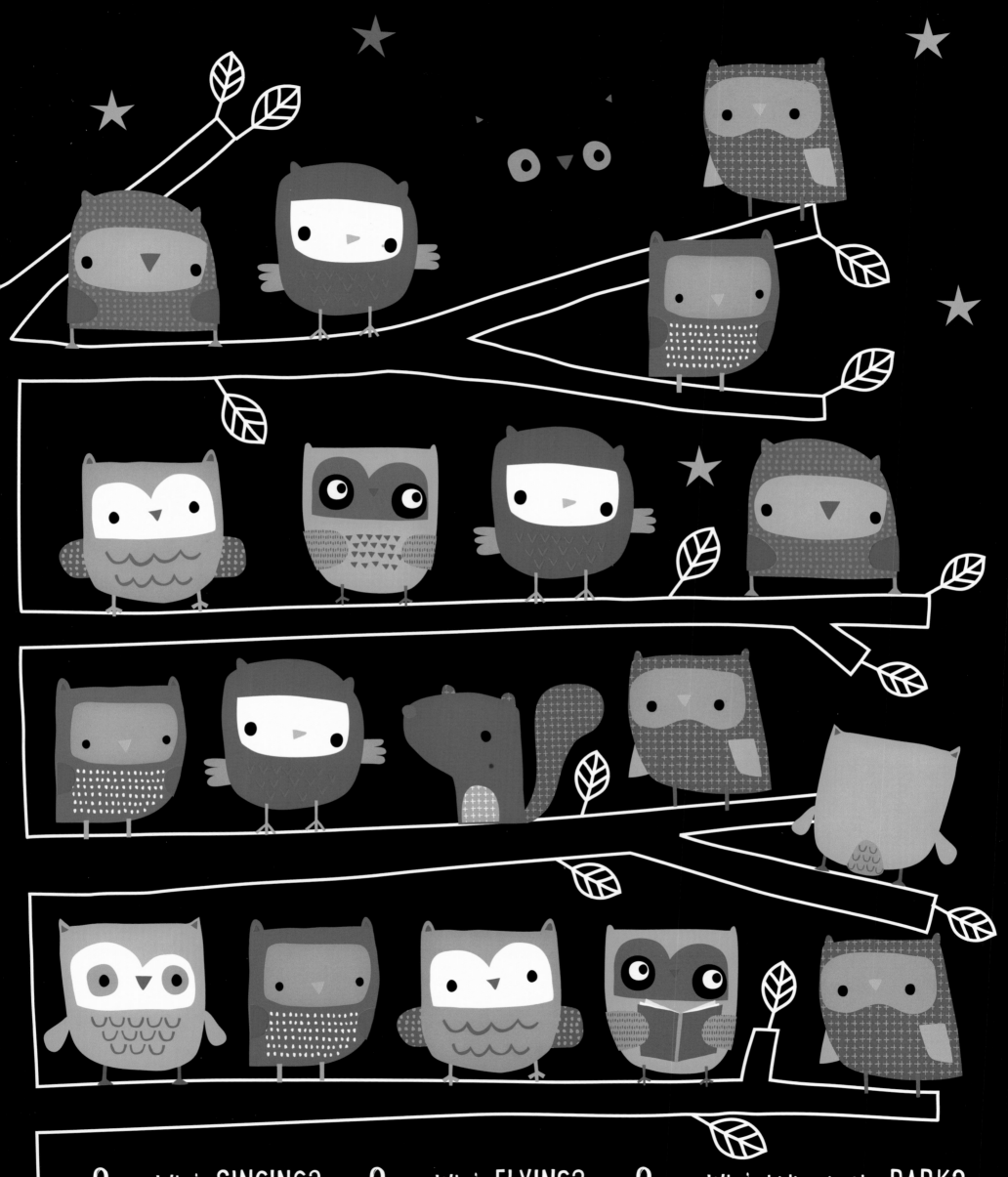

Who's SINGING? Who's FLYING? Who's hiding in the DARK?

PRETTY KITTIES

The cute little **KITTIES** love to **PURR**, with their long, fluffy WHISKERS and COLOURFUL **FUR**! **LOOK** up and down and try to find which wild cat is **ONE OF A KIND?**

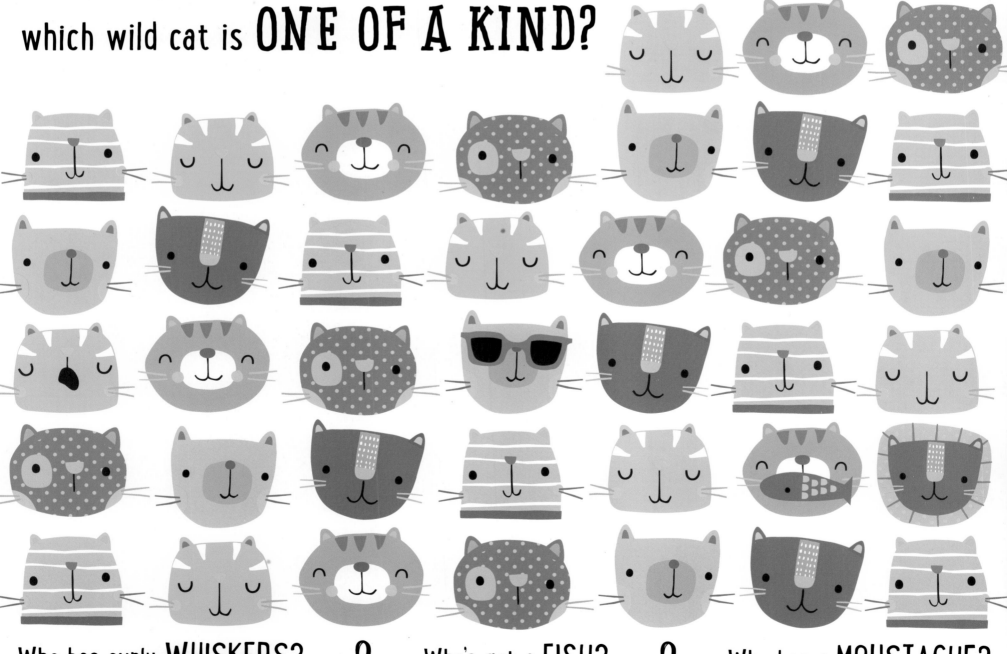

Who has curly WHISKERS?   Who's got a FISH?   Who has a MOUSTACHE?

Who's got a MOUSE? ⌇ Who's wearing SUNGLASSES? ⌇ Who's YAWNING?

INTO THE WILD

The wild animals are a COLOURFUL crew,
with BIG EARS and LONG NECKS
and FURRY MANES too!
LOOK up and down and try to find
which little creature is ONE OF A KIND?

Who's lost their SPOTS?   Who's facing the WRONG way?   Who's CRYING?

Who's lost their STRIPES?　　Who's ASLEEP?　　Who's wearing a HAT?

FUN ON THE FARM

There's so much to do in the FARMYARD today.
The CHICKENS need feeding,
the HORSES want HAY!
LOOK up and down and try to find
which blue animal is ONE OF A KIND?

Who hasn't HATCHED?   Who's lost their BABY?   Who has a FLOWER?

Who's wearing a stripy JUMPER? ❧ What's lost a WHEEL? ❧ Who has a CROWN?

HEAR ME ROAR!

WHAT can be making those **BIG, BOOMING** sounds?
It must be the **DINOSAURS,** stamping around!
LOOK up and down and try to find
which giant animal is **ONE OF A KIND?**

Who's brushing their **TEETH?** Who's got a **BONE?** Who's wearing a **BOW?**

Who's got a DOUGHNUT?   Who's lost their SPOTS?   Who's DANCING?

BOUNCING BUNNIES

The bouncing **BUNNIES** just love to JUMP!
They **HOP** and they LEAP
and then land with a **THUMP.**
LOOK up and down and try to find
which cute animal is **ONE OF A KIND?**

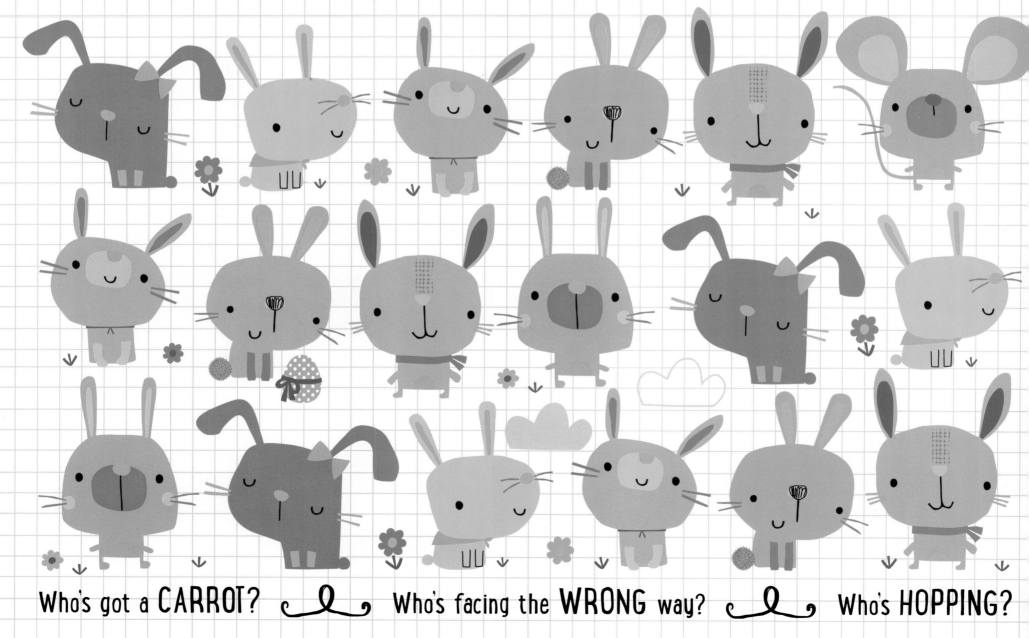

Who's got a CARROT?   Who's facing the WRONG way?   Who's HOPPING?

Who has big TEETH?　Who's got an EASTER EGG?　Who's wearing a HAT?

OUTER SPACE

In SPACE the STARS are twinkling bright.
The ROCKETS go WHOOSH
as they ZOOM through the night!
LOOK up and down and try to find
which space vehicle is ONE OF A KIND?

Which PLANET has lost its rings?   Who's UPSIDE DOWN?   Who has a PET?

Who's WAVING?   What's lost its STARS?   Who has a FLAG?

IN THE OCEAN

BLUE and GREEN creatures live under the sea.
They glide through the WATER
and SWIM peacefully!
LOOK up and down and try to find
which fierce fish is ONE OF A KIND?

Who's turned YELLOW?   Who's blowing BUBBLES?   Who's turned STRIPY?

Who's swimming UPSIDE DOWN?   Who's hiding inside their SHELL?

BEAUTIFUL BUGS

The BEAUTIFUL BUGS love to explore,
CREEPING and CRAWLING
down there on the FLOOR!
LOOK up and down and try to find
which hopping creature is ONE OF A KIND?

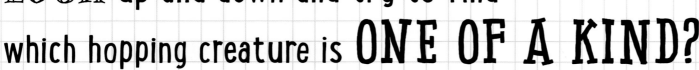

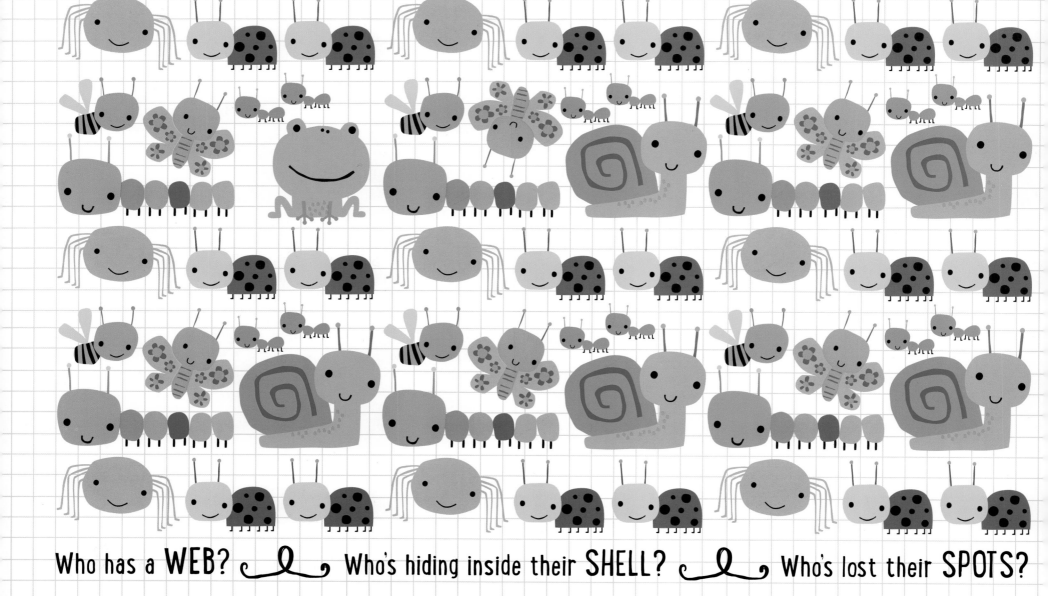

Who has a WEB?　　Who's hiding inside their SHELL?　　Who's lost their SPOTS?

Who's flying UPSIDE DOWN? Who's wearing colourful BOOTS?

IN THE WASH

The SUN is out and the WEATHER is fine.
The CLOTHES are all HANGING
to DRY on the LINE!
LOOK up and down and try to find
which piece of washing is ONE OF A KIND?

What's lost its BOBBLE?   What's missing a BUTTON?   What's turned RED?

What's lost its **STRIPES?**   What's **SHRUNK?**   What's lost a **FLOWER?**

HOME, SWEET HOME

The **HOUSES** in town are lovely and bright, with beautiful WINDOWS that **GLOW** through the night. **LOOK** up and down and try to find which grand house is **ONE OF A KIND?**

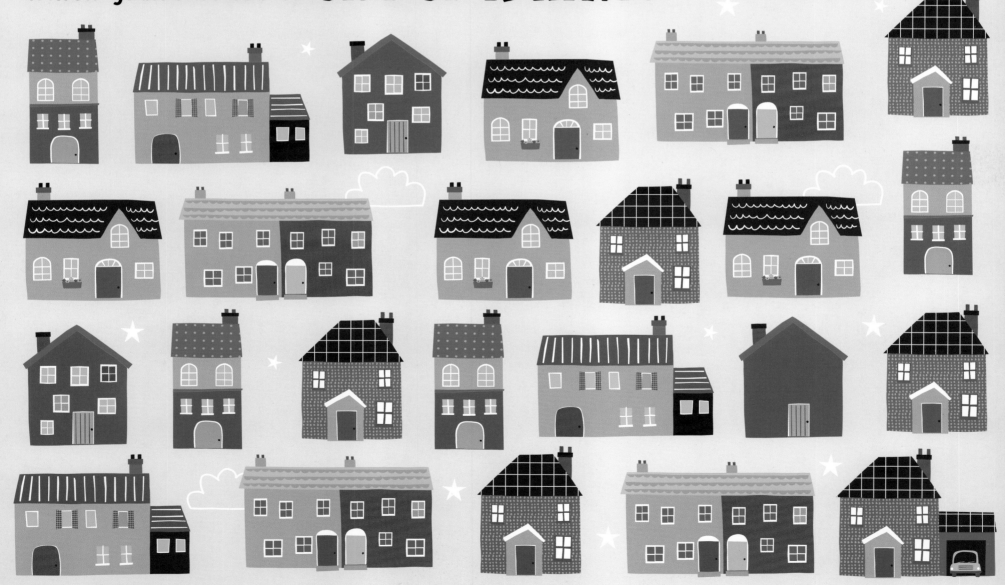

Which CHIMNEY is puffing smoke?

Which house has no WINDOWS?

Where is the CAT?   Which CHIMNEY is very tall?   Where is the CAR?